Publications International, Ltd.

Illustrations: Dave Garbot, Larry Jones, Robbie Short

Louis Weber, CEO
Publications International, Ltd.
7373 North Cicero Avenue
Lincolnwood, Illinois 60712

ISBN-13: 978-1-4508-2404-0
ISBN-10: 1-4508-2404-8

Manufactured in China.

8 7 6 5 4 3 2 1

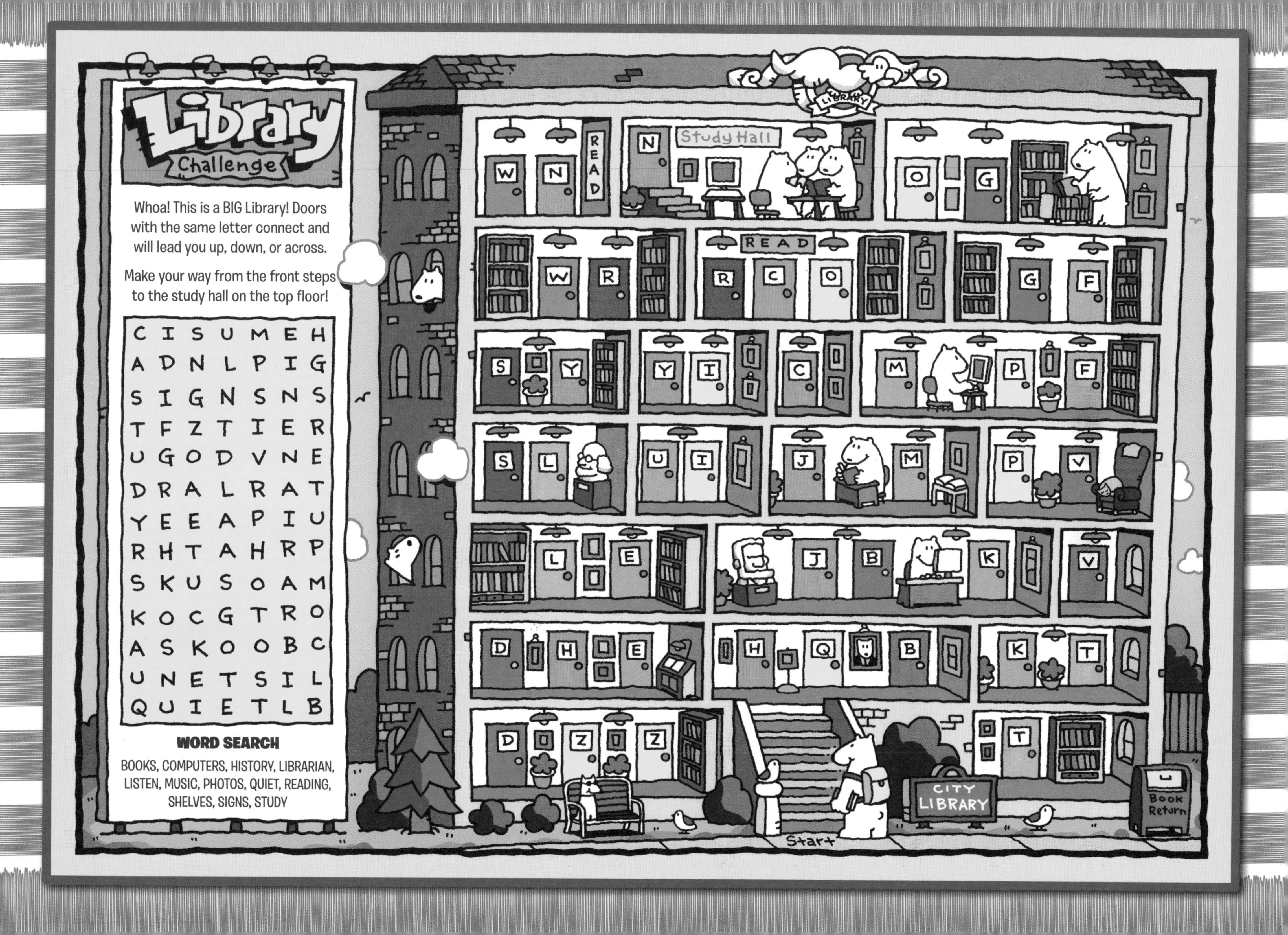
Library
Challenge
Whoa! This is a BIG Library! Doors with the same letter connect and will lead you up, down, or across.
Make your way from the front steps to the study hall on the top floor!
C I S U M E H
A D N L P I G
S I G N S N S
T F Z T I E R
U G O D V N E
D R A L R A T
Y E E A P I U
R H T A H R P
S K U S O A M
K O C G T R O
A S K O O B C
U N E T S I L
Q U I E T L B
WORD SEARCH
BOOKS, COMPUTERS, HISTORY, LIBRARIAN, LISTEN, MUSIC, PHOTOS, QUIET, READING, SHELVES, SIGNS, STUDY
LIBRARY
Study Hall
READ
READ
CITY LIBRARY
Book Return
Start

Tookie Bird Safari
START
Help the explorers find the sneaky Tookie Bird.
FINISH

What's the Message?
Use the code to fill in the letters on the lines below to reveal a message just for you!
A E F H L O
P R S T W
Answer: Please water the flowers
Start
Back to the Hive!
This honeybee is lost in the garden. Help him find his way back to the Hive by tracing the correct blue line.
Hive

Find the two camels that match!
1.
2.
3.
4.
5.
6.
7.
8.
9.
10.
Answer: Numbers 2 and 9
Oh Mummy!
This mummy went on a trip, but he can't remember how to get home! Help him find his way, but first stop at the grocery store and then at the vet to pick up his pooch.
Finish
VET
Grocery
?
Start

Finish
BIG TOP
challenge!
The Flying Bears are ready to perform, but one of their members is still on the ground! Help this bear choose the right rope for his climb up top!
The HUMAN Cannon BALL!
FLYING BEARS
FLYING BEARS
FLYING BEARS
NO WAY!
FLEA
10
10
Find
Start

Fe-Fi-Fo-FUM!
START
(Don't cross any yellow lines!)
Help this poor giant get his goose back from that THIEVIN' JACK!
FINISH!
Unscramble these Fairy-Tale Folks!
INREDLACEL
ETH HETER TILELT SIGP
LIPEGESN TAYEBU
TREEP NAP
IHOPCOINC
NWSO THEWI
HEMROT OSOGE
YTMUPH PUDTYM
EHT IGB DBA FOWL
Answers: Cinderella, The Three Little Pigs, Sleeping Beauty, Peter Pan, Pinocchio, Snow White, Mother Goose, Humpty Dumpty, The Big Bad Wolf

The Great Dino
COOKIE CHASE
Start
Finish

TreeHouse
MAZE·O·RAMA
Whoa! Cool treehouse! Help this climber from bottom to top. How many bears can you spot along the way?
Who?
FINISH
OUT OF ORDER
Start
Answer: 8

ROAD TRIP
MAZE
These three New York City Bears are driving across the USA to Los Angeles! They want to visit six other cities along the way. The cities are listed below, but not in the right order. Write the names of the cities in the correct order the Bears will visit them. Then help them find their way to LA!
1 ______
2 ______
3 ______
4 ______
5 ______
6 ______
Canada AY?
U.P.
MINT
GRAND OLE OPRY
Start
NY
Moo
END
Los Angeles
SUPER DOME
Mexico Si?
Hola
Gulf of Mexico
Answers: 1. Chicago 2. Nashville 3. Dallas 4. New Orleans 5. Denver 6. Seattle

A DAY AT THE ZOO
Hey, they left the door open!
Let's find the bananas!
START
GIRAFFE
LION
FINISH
CAN YOU FIND THE 14 BANANAS
HIDDEN IN THIS MAZE?

Pumpkin Patch
CHALLENGE
We found our pumpkins! Now help us get through the patch and the corn maze to the EXIT!
START
Sorry— GO BACK
Nope
CORN MAZE
Oops
EXIT

ON THE FARM
It's dinnertime!
Help Bossy back to the barn.
START
FINISH

PASTA-MAN-IA
Mama Mia, that's a lot of spaghetti! Find your way from our hungry eater to the spicy meatball at the end!
YUM!
FINISH

Where's Charlie?
Oh, no! My hamster, Charlie, got out! Can you help me find him?
Start
Finish

Witch Way?!!
KITTY
HELP!
This witch's kitty is stuck! Can you help her find the way to the rescue?
START
Can you find nine bats on this page?
FIND THESE SPOOKY WORDS!
(SIDEWAYS, UP, DOWN, BACKWARDS, AND DIAGONALLY)
J G Y D P B Z P K G R E U
W A E I S E M G H O S T N
E U R O L I A M T U J C H
N F I W E R E W O L F E B
N Q P E K U L H M P L M K
A Y M M U M D N I L B O G
F R A N K E N S T E I N F
A M V D T C S A Z D T S I
B H V N O T E L E K S T R
O R U U F X Z O M B I E Q
B A T L O Z H N W V H R Y
H L V D Q N O D N A L X S
BAT, FRANKENSTEIN, GHOST, GOBLIN, HAUNTED HOUSE,
MONSTER, MUMMY, SKELETON, VAMPIRE, WEREWOLF, ZOMBIE

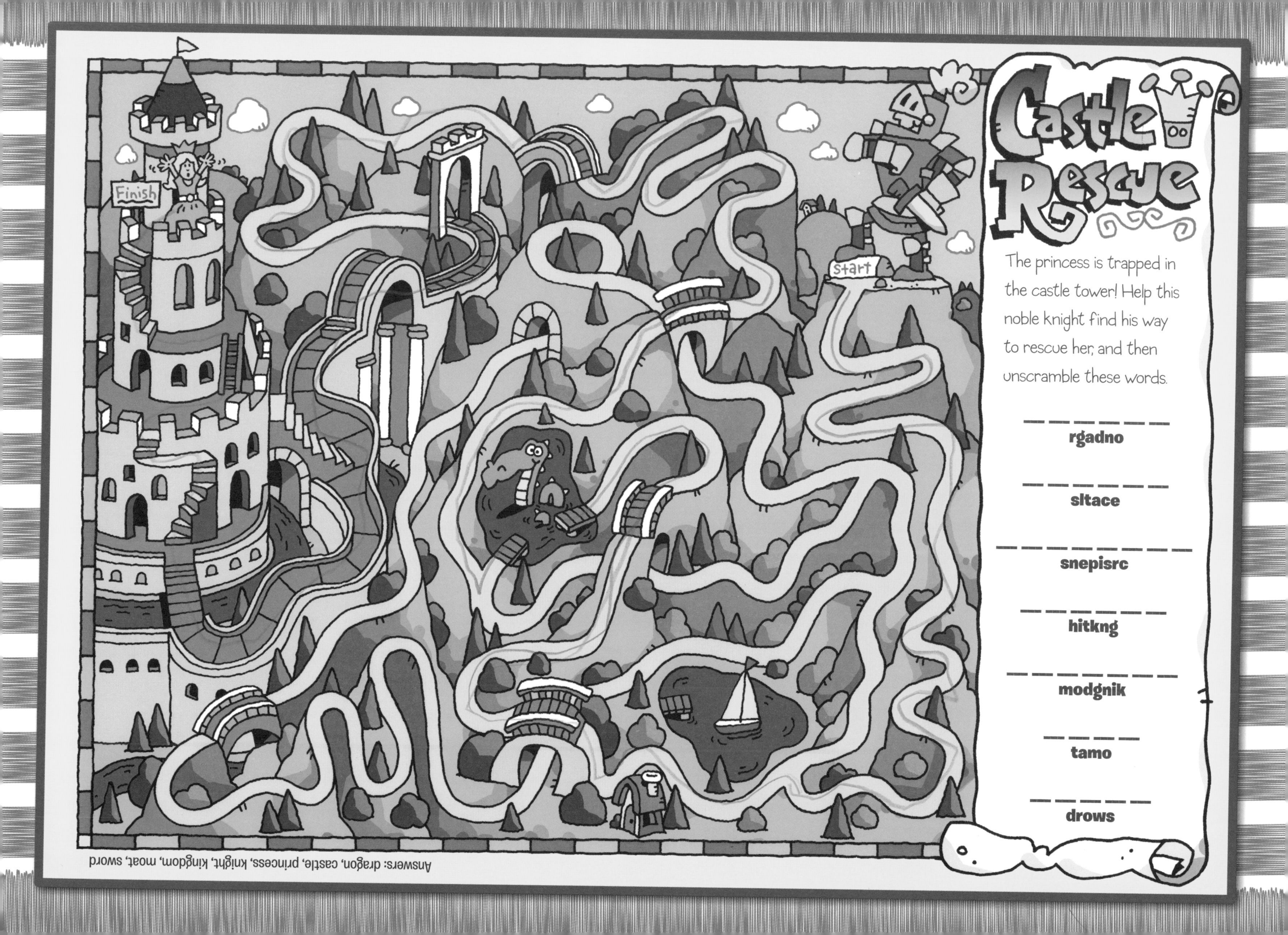
Castle Rescue
Finish
Start
The princess is trapped in the castle tower! Help this noble knight find his way to rescue her, and then unscramble these words.
rgadno
sltace
snepisrc
hitkng
modgnik
tamo
drows
Answers: dragon, castle, princess, knight, kingdom, moat, sword

Collect all the letters from the pennants and unscramble them to find out what happens next!
Eight letters
DECODE HERE
!
We got great tickets! Help us find our seats.
START
FINISH
B
Y
I
L
A
L
P
A
It's the BIG GAME!
Answer: Play ball!

Rover's Lost!
Oh, no! Rover has wandered off again, and he can't remember how to get back. Help him find his way home for dinner. Then solve these word puzzles.
1. +
2. + + S
3. +
4. + + R
start
IN
OUT
Nope
ROVER!
Answers: 1. birdhouse 2. eyeglasses 3. moonlight 4. dogcatcher

SNOW-DAY!
Which one of these scattered skiers
will reach the finish?
START
END
SOLVE THE
SNEAKY SNOWFLAKE!
FINISH
FIRST FILL IN THE BLANKS,
AND THEN READ THIS
flaky story
Yesterday, we had the weirdest snow ever! The ____________ (adjective)
snowflakes were made of ____________ (noun) and ____________ (large number) feet
of them covered the ground. Everyone put on their ____________ (plural noun)
and ran out in the snow. We grabbed our ____________ (plural noun) and ran outside.
On my first ride from the top of a ____________ (something tiny), I got up to ____________ (large number) miles an
hour and then crashed right into a ____________ (noun)! After that we decided to have a snowball
battle, but instead of snow, we threw ____________ (plural noun) at each other! Then we built a snowman out of
____________ (noun). Sadly, the sun came out and began to ____________ (verb) all the snow away. "Oh well,"
we said, "We can always ____________ (verb) in the puddles!"

QUEST for FUEL
Zoob is running out of fuel!
Help him find the way to the station.
START
FINISH
FUEL

School Map
This new student needs to get to the cafeteria, but first he has to stop in the math, science, and history rooms in that order. Use the School Map to help him find his way!
Cafeteria
MILK
English
History
P.E.
Math
Science
1st
Start
School Map
B D O G B N E G
X F M V S D S B
H C N U L S W O
E A T H I U J O
A S R E C Z A K
D C R A N B C S
L T O B E A T E
N R E D P S E S
O O B K Z C M N
T T C A T I O T
E A M O P S E O
B L E R A S E R
O U H E Y O S U
O C N I A R T L
K L L N B S U E
P A P E R C L R
W C L I P S O N
WORD SEARCH
BACKPACK, BOOKS, CALCULATOR, ERASER, LUNCH, NOTEBOOK, PAPER, PENCILS, RULER, SCISSORS

Take A WILD RIDE!
Ride the Zoom-A-Loop all the way to the finish!
START
ZOOM·A·LOOP
Unscramble the safety rule for a free ride!
NAGH NO GITHT, SLPAEE!
ZOOM·A·LOOP
FINISH
Answer: Hang on tight, please!

5¢
MONSTER MAZE
NO. 1
CONQUER THE GLORP-MONSTER FROM PLANET ZORT!
START
FINISH
IT'S AN INVASION!!!
Follow one set of aliens from the moon to the earth, and another back to the moon! You can move up, down, sideways, and diagonally!
CREATURE FEATURES!
WHICH TWO ARE IDENTICAL?

Get to
Gramma's House!
Little Red Riding Hood is on her way to Gramma's House with dinner. Help Red find her way through the woods. Then use the code below to see what she brought in her basket for dinner!
A B D E G H I
L M N P S T
Start Here
WRONG WAY RED
Quiet Please
INFO
Gramma's House
Answer: Spaghetti and Meatballs

Fishy Friends
Help the angelfish find his friends.
START
ZZZ
FINISH

EVEREST
CHALLENGE
Help these climbers to the top of the world! Be sure to stop at each campsite along the way.
Mt. Everest
A
B
C
GO BACK
Start
Watch Your Step!
Climbing BONUS
Only six rocks on this climb have numbers that don't touch a rock with the same number. Can you find them?

In the TOY STORE
We're shopping for scooters!
TODAY ONLY!
SPECIAL
BIG SALE!
START
HALF OFF!
MARKED DOWN
RMQUSGHI
DOLLCYDT
HGFMOVXR
COWBOYDA
ZDNJTERI
SPACEMAN
TOVARBEP
GFDTDNBD
ECOWGIRL
Find the hidden words:
BEAR COWGIRL SCOOTER
CAT DOG SPACEMAN
COWBOY DOLL TRAIN
SALE
SOLD OUT
FINISH
MARKED DOWN

GOOD LUCK!
Follow the rainbow from start to finish!
Can you find 15 4-leaf clovers?
START
FINISH
A CHARMING CHALLENGE!
Study the pattern and fill in the blank squares so that each row has each charm only once!

GOING BUGGY!
START!
HER MAJESTY NEEDS HELP! THIS POOR ANT QUEEN HAS BEEN WORKING THE NURSERY ALL DAY, AND SHE'S HUNGRY! HELP THE WORKER ANTS GET FOOD TO THEIR QUEEN.
WHICH SHADOW DOESN'T MATCH ITS ANT?
STOP! IN ORDER TO CONTINUE, FIRST DECIPHER THESE CODES:
+ R + -O+R
- Tash + +
Butterfly
Caterpillar
mosquitto
ANSWERS: BUTTERFLY, CATERPILLAR, MOSQUITO

PARADE!
SEE IF YOU CAN FIND YOUR WAY TO THE FRONT BY MOVING THROUGH THE CONFETTI AND BALLOONS.
START
CAN YOU SPOT THE SEVEN THINGS THAT ARE DIFFERENT AMONG THE TRUMPET PLAYERS?
UNSCRAMBLE THE LETTERS FROM THE BALLOONS OF THE SAME COLOR TO READ THE MESSAGE.
ASRPADE RAE SYAWLA LTSO FO UFN!
FINISH
ANSWER: PARADES ARE ALWAYS LOTS OF FUN!

HOP TO IT!!!
Get from the first pad to the second!
Start
End
LUCKY BUG!
Follow one type of bug from one flower and a different bug back to the first flower...but watch out for hungry frogs! It is okay to move diagonally.
Froggy Funnies!
What's a frog's favorite kind of music?
Hip-hop!
What does a frog feel like when he steps in tree sap?
Un-hoppy!
What's a frog's favorite sport?
"Croak-ay"

Visit The
Museum Maze
Welcome to the Museum!
Find your way from the entrance to the exit, but be sure to visit the Dinosaur, Art, Heart, Egypt, Space, Automobiles, and Sculpture Exhibits, then the Museum Gift Shop – in that order – before you leave!
SCULPTURE
The Bear
ART
SPACE
DINOSAURS
GIFTS
MUS E UM
EXIT
ENTER
HEART
Thump Thump
EGYPT
AUTOMOBILES
MUS E UM

Web Sweet Web
It's time for school! Where's my book bag?
Start
Finish
Find the hidden pictures: baseball, caterpillar, horn, ladybug, lightbulb, paintbrush, pencil, surfboard

MAD SCIENCE!
START
FIND THREE AMOEBAS THAT ARE IDENTICAL.
IT'S A CHEMICAL CONUNDRUM! THIS MAD PROFESSOR HAS DISCOVERED A HAIR-GROWTH TONIC FOR FROGS! NAVIGATE THROUGH THE MAZE, PICKING UP EACH ITEM FOR HIS CONCOCTION. BUT DON'T PASS EACH ONE MORE THAN ONCE OR THE RESULTS COULD PROVE DISASTROUS!!!
Figure out why the frogs don't like the new tonic...
TI KEASM MHTE PYJMU!
__ _____ ____ _____!
FINISH
Answer: It makes them jumpy!

River
RUNNERS
Let's Go!
START
P O E P P B M K I B
V A U O N D S A C I
C H D R N D L Y S E
A L A D I A T A K K
J F M P L E C K C W
T V A Z M E C A O N
P R N L G O T R R D
E L E E E X W Z R Y
L H L W P E V A W B
N J C N C T X O V K
Find these words:
CANOE
HELMET
KAYAK
PADDLE
RAFT
RAPID
ROCKS
WAVE
No way I'm running that! Can you help me get down the rocks?
Start
I flipped over! Can you help me find my: sunscreen, helmet, paddles (2), sunglasses, life vest, water bottle, shoes (2), and sandwich?
FINISH

Arrrggghh!s
"X"
marks the spot!
Sail ye ship to the treasure and make
sure to stop for supplies once on each island...
but be wary of sharks, skeletons, and sea monsters!!!
START
SUPPLIES
SUPPLIES
SUPPLIES
X
How many gold doubloons like
this one can you find on this page?
Question: What did the ocean say to the sea captain?
Answer: Nothing- It just waved!